LANDMARK COLLECTOR'S LIBRARY

Collieries

of Somerset & Bristol

John Cornwell

Cantilevered headframe, Old Mills Colliery, 1665

LANDMARK COLLECTOR'S LIBRARY

COLLIERIES
OF SOMERSET & BRISTOL

John Cornwell

Landmark Publishing

Published by
Landmark Publishing Ltd,
Ashbourne Hall, Cokayne Ave
Ashbourne, Derbyshire DE6 1EJ England
Tel: (01335) 347349 Fax: (01335) 347303
e-mail: landmark@clara.net
web site: www.landmarkpublishing.co.uk

1st edition

ISBN 1 84306 029 9

British Library Cataloguing in Publication Data: a catalogue
record for this book is available from the British Library.

Printed by MPG Ltd, Bodmin, Cornwall

Design & reproduction by James Allsopp

Cover captions:

Front cover: Writhington Colliery, 1968
Back cover Top: Spare sheave waiting to be raised upon new headframe, 1938

ACKNOWLEDGEMENTS

The bulk of the photographs in this book were taken by the author over the years 1965 to 1974. The high quality underground photographs in Kilmersdon and Writhlington Collieries and Harry Stoke Mine; the surface photographs of Mendip Colliery, and one or two other surface photographs, were taken around 1960-61 by Nigel Booth, the son of the Group Manager of the National Coal Board.

I should also like to thank Ray Ashman for permission to use his two photographs at Norton Hill Colliery and the photograph of the sinking of the Harry Stoke Mine, and Alex Hann for the photograph on page 108.

CONTENTS

INTRODUCTION

Much has been published on the early days of coal mining in the Bristol and Somerset coalfield, but little has been written on the years under the National Coal Board.

The activities of the National Coal Board in Bristol and Somerset over 26 years are now becoming a distant memory and will soon be forgotten. The only record at the present time is the *History of the Somerset Coalfield* by Down and Warrington, which has long been out of print and is almost impossible to obtain.

This book is an attempt to record the activity of the National Coal Board in the Bristol and Somerset coalfield. The last collieries, Kilmersdon and Writhlington, closed in 1973, and each year the remaining ex - NCB personnel become thinner on the ground.

In 1959 the area office at Woodborough House was closed and much valuable material was destroyed. Later in 1985 when the NCB survey office at the Old Norton Pit closed further records were destroyed, and more was removed to South Wales and was lost.

So in the year 2001, I felt what information remained should be published for posterity. The bulk of the information in this book is held by Bristol Coalmining Archives Limited, a company established to provide mining reports to the legal profession.

Although the book covers the years of Nationalisation the earlier years are also mentioned as early developments, particularly shaft sinking and main roads, were greatly affected later planning decisions made by the National Coal Board.

The Bristol and Somerset Coalfield was different from most other coalfields in the Great Britain. The pits had a distinct Somerset Style, and were usually built of local White Lias and often in attractive rural settings. Although small, they had a certain charm, and I feel that they were an interesting addition to the landscape. Most of the buildings dated from the mid to late nineteenth century. Unfortunately few remains of the thirteen pits now exist; although a number of older pre-NCB pits with substantial structures remain. Often only the spoil heaps survive, and they are covered by trees.

The reserves of most pits were almost exhausted by Nationalisation (1947), and all were suffering from lack of investment during World War II; they had not been mechanised like the larger pits in South Wales, the Midlands and Yorkshire. Although the pits were losing money and outdated, the workforce was dedicated and had a distinct identity. The men worked in conditions which would not have been tolerated in other areas. The Somerset miners were a unique body of men, who could and did work in thin poor seams, extremely poor conditions and with outdated equipment. Recently an ex-NCB official stated that a team of men transferred from Camerton Colliery were the finest men that he had ever worked with.

The miners' housing in Somerset, particularly in Radstock, which was mainly built by the Waldegrave family, and which eventually became Coal Board housing was bright and extremely pleasant. It was a cut above much of the coal industry housing in other areas.

The comment by Nikolaus Pevsner that Radstock is really desperately ugly, and is without dignity, is extremely unfair. Having viewed coalfield housing across the country, I would say that Radstock is a pleasant town, and that industrial housing by the Waldegrave family is extremely attractive.

It is highly unlikely that Pevsner saw the housing in South Wales and other coalfields. Few coalfields could boast of pits like Writhlington and Camerton with their associated housing set in such attractive rolling countryside.

I would also like to record that the Somerset and Bristol Group of the National Coal Board in its early days was a good employer; few people now realise that Ludlows Pit was kept open for some years solely to provide employment for the men. The original local management was comprised of people with a local background and deep feeling for the area.

The Nationalisation of the coalfield certainly extended the life of the main pits , as the original owners could not have provided the large amount of investment which was needed. The investment that the NCB made available prolonged the life of the main pits by another 26 years.

Unfortunately there was now an insufficient number of miners for the diminishing number of pits, which had dropped from thirteen at Vesting Date to six in 1960; with poor geology and the new massive reserves in Warwickshire and Yorkshire, the fate of the Bristol and Somerset Coalfield was sealed, although Polish and others, and later Durham miners, were brought into the coalfield in an attempt to raise the numbers of the workforce.

Although the last colliery, Kilmersdon and Writhlington, closed in 1973, this was not the end of the coalfield. The NCB Survey office continued was working on the site of the Old Pit at Norton Hill, providing mining reports and dealing with subsidence and shaft filling.

The Office was staffed by the late Don Dowding, who commenced work at Old Mills Colliery, under William Evans Co, and Ray Ashman who had been the surveyor at the four pits of the Somerset Collieries Ltd: Braysdown, Camerton, Radstock (Ludlows) and Norton Hill Colliery. They were backed up by Anne Rabbitts of Oakhill, whose father had been the shaftsman at Mendip Colliery. The survey office was closed by British Coal in 1986, bringing to an end many years of Somerset mining.

The retired miners are now elderly. Royalties from the first edition of this book have been gifted to the Somerset District Miners Welfare Trust, which is a charity devoted to the helping those who have been employed in Somerset in the Coal Mining Industry.

John Cornwell
Hallatrow
North East Somerset

Electric Winder House, Kilmersdon Colliery, 1972-3

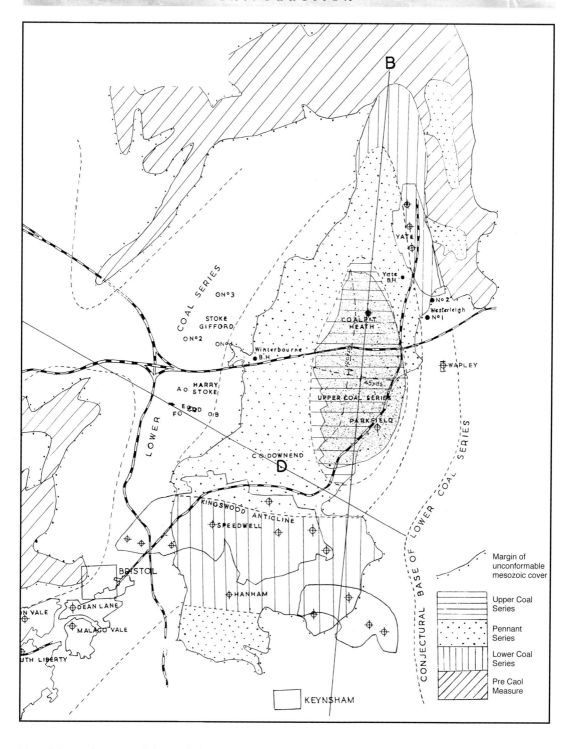

Map of the north portion of the Coalfield showing the Harry Stoke Mine and Coalpit Heath Colliery with the railway system and abandoned pits.

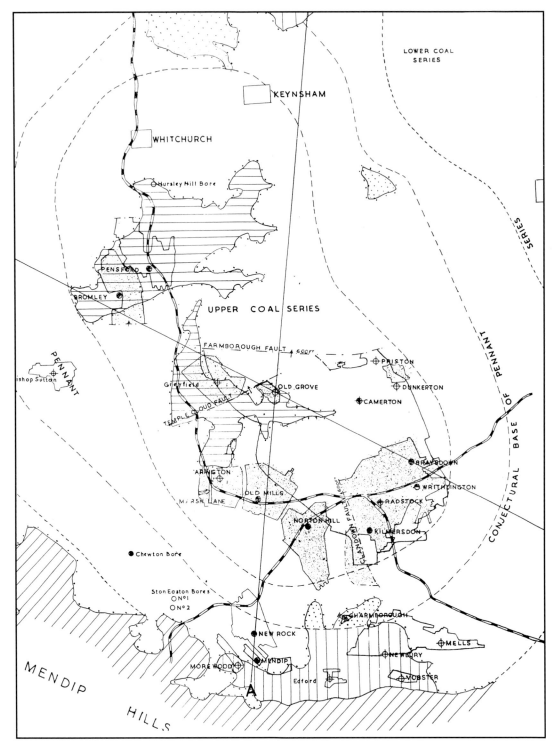

Map of the southern portion of the Coalfield showing NCB pits at vesting date and other closed pits.

BRAYSDOWN COLLIERY, RADSTOCK, SOMERSET

The original winding shaft of this colliery was begun in 1840. The shaft was sunk with a diameter of 5 ft and a depth of 678 ft down to the Bull Seam. The pumping shaft was commenced around the same time 120 ft to the south east of the winding shaft. This shaft was also 5 ft in diameter and 690 ft in depth, including the sump. The shaft was used for downcast and pumping. Both shafts were lined with Lias limestone and hydraulic lime mortar. Little water was met with in the sinking.

The quantity of coal raised in the one small shaft was very limited and from the financial point of view the colliery was profitless. In 1860 a 10 ft diameter shaft was commenced and sunk to open out the Farrington group of seams. This shaft was placed right under the 5 ft winding shaft, the east side coinciding with the right hand side of the 5 ft shaft. In 1866 an air shaft was begun in order to make a second connection between the Farrington and Radstock groups. This air shaft was also 5 ft in diameter and was driven upwards for the whole of its height, starting in the No. 4 Farrington Seam, until it holed into a stone drift prepared to meet it. This stone drift emerged near the bottom of the pumping shaft. In 1869 a twin shaft 5 ft in diameter was sunk alongside the old winding shaft, 8 inches of brickwork constituting the only division between the old and new shafts. The sinking was continued down to the Bull Seam, while coaling was continued for 10 hours daily in the old shaft. The 10 ft shaft and the twin shafts above it then formed the upcast for the whole of the mine, with one cage descending through the old 5 ft and 10 ft shaft below it, while the other ascended through the 10 ft and the new 5 ft shaft above it. The shaft was later sunk to a final depth of 1834 feet.

The original winding engine was beam type, with a 30 in cylinder and a 5 ft stroke, with two 12 ft plain drums. This engine could raise 150 tons of coal and 60 tons of debris plus 40 tons of water in one day. The pumping engine was of the Cornish type built by Winwood of Bristol and was erected at Braysdown in 1845, but had been previously at work at the old colliery at Newton St Loe. This engine had a 60 in cylinder and 8 ft stroke. The engine only worked one and a half hours in twenty four, and raised water in three forcing lifts from the sump under the Bull Seam, a depth of 690 ft.

The beam engine was later replaced by a twin cylinder winding engine by J. D. Leigh, with a similar engine on the second shaft. The colliery was later connected to Camerton Colliery and a further connection with Ludlows Pit. The last years of the colliery under the National Coal Board saw little change, the workings were very extensive and extended out under Peasedown St John and were bounded on the west by Camerton and Ludlows Collieries which were connected to Braysdown.

At Nationalisation in 1947 the saleable output of coal was 37,250 tons, in 1948 the output was still only 37,534 tons. By 1949 the output had dropped to 31,580 tons, but by 1950 the figure had risen to 43,234 tons. The loss for 1950 was £15,426 .

The colliery closed in 1959.

Early drawing of Braysdown Colliery showing the original beam winding house and typical Somerset pithead built of Lias; the headframe appears to be wooden. The shaft shows the two sinkings with the brick wall between them.

Pre-nationalisation photograph of Braysdown Pit, showing the striking battlemented gateway which enclosed the colliery yard and pithead.

Disused winding engine house in 1968.

Bromley was an early sinking and was said to have been sunk around 1860. The first record of the pit was the geological map of 1871 which shows a coal pit on the site. The name of the original firm who sank the colliery is not known.

The Colliery was the smallest of the Somerset pits and was said to have been a prosperous undertaking. Little information is now available on this colliery which at its best only raised 1,655 tons of coal in November 1949, but only 892 and 853 tons were raised in August and September of 1950, from a coaling shaft 4 ft 6 ins in diameter and 474 ft in depth.

The colliery was clearly not suited to any form of modernisation. It had small diameter shafts and a poor underground layout and the reserves could be worked from Pensford Colliery. Bromley Colliery was closed in 1957, with three of the four pit ponies been taken into retirement; the fourth was retained for another few months removing machinery, rails, steel roof supports and other salvageable material to the shaft bottom. At closure the colliery employed 80 men who produced 500 tons of coal per week. Almost all of the men were transferred to Pensford Colliery.

The colliery had one winding engine house which had only one winding engine for the two shafts, situated north and south of the engine house, which has now been converted into a dwelling. The winder was steam powered and a battery of three Lancashire boilers was situated alongside the engine house. The output of the mine was taken to Pensford Colliery on a two feet gauge tramway which was worked by a haulage engine operating a main-and-tail rope system at the Pensford end of the tramway.

Pit ponies at Bromley Colliery, late 1956. Mr Tovey on the left.

Camerton Colliery, like Ludlows and Bromley Pits, was little affected by the Nationalisation of the coal industry and on the surface little or no changes took place until the colliery ceased working in 1950.

There were two pits at Camerton, each with two shafts, the Old and New Pits. The Old Pit, which was sunk in the 1780s, was closed as a coaling pit in the late 1890s, but was used as an emergency exit until the pit was finally abandoned in 1937 when the site was dismantled.

The New Pit was sunk sometime around 1800 and worked five seams all in the Radstock series of seams, The Great, Top Little, Middle, Slyving and Under Little. Deep workings in the Farrington Series were opened, but were soon abandoned after only a few thousand tons of coal were worked. See page 16, where the shaft section shows the heading driven through four of the Farrington seams.

The take of the New Pit was very large being two and a half miles north to south, and one and a half miles east to west. The furthest point reached by the workings to the south was the Fosse Way. On the east of the Camerton take the workings were bounded by those of Dunkerton Colliery. To the west of the take the workings were bounded by Upper and Lower Conygre Collieries.

Most of the Somerset Collieries were affected by adverse geology, but at Camerton Colliery it was the reverse, here a succession of upthrow faults to the south of the shafts enabled the main haulage road from the pit bottom to run southwards with little or no dip, which certainly reduced the cost of the dip workings. See page 16 for a plan showing the various seams.

It was a naked light mine and candles were in use at Camerton by one or two older men up to closure, although the majority use the carbide light.

The pit was almost exhausted by Nationalisation and little modernisation was undertaken although undercutting machines and additional conveyors were brought in. The *Somerset Guardian* reported in 1950 that many of the men felt that there was plenty of workable coal left, but when the NUM brought in an independent engineer to examine the pit, he could find no evidence that would justify keeping the pit open.

The colliery output in the last 3 years was poor. In 1947, 32,264 saleable tons were raised with 32,238 tons in 1948 and with a slight increase in 1949 to 34,494 tons. The colliery closed on 15 April 1950, with most of the men moving to Norton Hill Colliery.

Today, apart from the heapstead, the only remaining building is the colliery canteen, now used a dwelling, and Newpit Cottages with the pump which was used for the domestic water supply still to be seen under the tramway archway between the cottages.

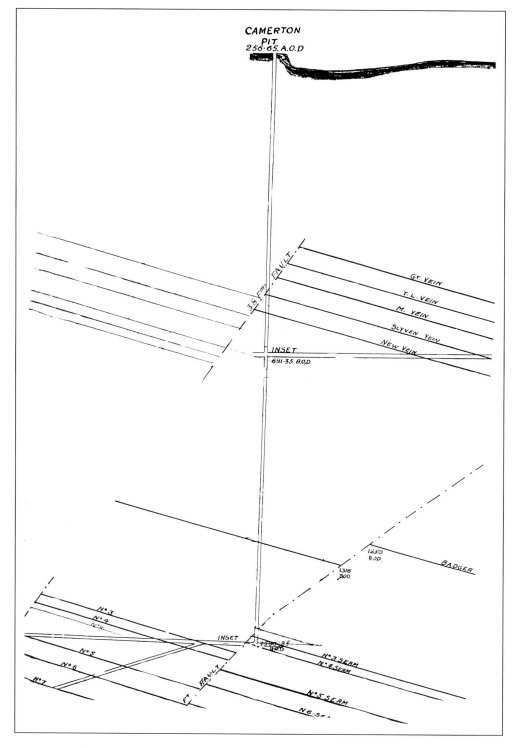

Camerton Colliery. A section of Camerton Pit showing the drivage into the deep Farrington seams which were abandoned after working only a few thousand tons of coal.

An extremely rare photograph of 1938, of the replacing of the wooden headframe with a larger steel headframe, which was erected over the wooden frame; this would allow the rope and guides to be changed over a week end or holiday without interrupting the winding of coal.

Spare sheave waiting to be raised upon the new headframe, 1938.

Shaftsmen waiting to descend the shaft during the construction of the replacement headframe in 1938.

Camerton Colliery before Nationalisation. A journey of empty tubs stands in the foreground with a pitpony; this pit layout and buildings never changed apart from replacing the wooden headframe with a steel structure.

CHARMBOROUGH COLLIERY, CHARMBOROUGH, SOMERSET

This slant was sunk and owned by Charmborough Collieries Ltd on the outcrop of the No.2 seam of the Lower Coal series. The mine site was located on the eastern side of the Charlton to Holcombe Road just to the east of Southmead Farm.

The mine proved three seams, but only worked the first two, the Newbury No. 1, which was 20 to 24 ins thick, and the No. 2 Vein which was 39 ins to 46 ins thick. The No. 3 vein (20 ins thick), was not worked at Charmborough, but worked in a limited way nearby at Holcombe Wood.

The coaling drift was driven with a diameter of 8 feet, and was 1,650 feet in length with an extremely steep dip. The entrance was 500 feet to the north west of a small east-west fault. 400 feet to the south a larger fault curved to the south east, with a third fault 2,000 feet to the east running north-south. The workable coal was confined to a triangular area of ground which was small even by Somerset standards, and with extensive faulting and overturned strata, the quality of coal deposits was doubtful.

There were two slants known as Hamworthy Slant located to the east of the main slant. They appear to have been driven some time before Charmborough, and may have been an abandoned unproductive working, which was used for ventilation purposes.

The mine cannot be said to have been successful and only raised 7,833 tons in 1946; the average tonnage was about 100 tons per week. The NCB nationalised the colliery in January 1947, and closed it later in the same year.

Plans of the mine have recently come to light which show that it was proposed to reopen the mine in the 1950s and work some of the seams with a modern layout of panels and gate roads. It was expected to take a year to work out a panel and the dates of 1951,1952 and 53 were shown on the plan. Clearly the scheme, which was totally impracticable, came to nothing and the mine was never reopened.

When this colliery was taken into public ownership in 1947 it was clear that it was almost ex
hausted. The two main seams, the High and Hard Veins, were almost worked out and the remaining seam, the Hollybush, was known to be disturbed with poor roof conditions.

This colliery was originally sunk by the Coalpit Heath Collieries around 1852/3 to the north of an
area which had been previously worked by the Company. Frog Lane Pit was worked with Mays Hill
Colliery, an earlier pit, which is known to have been at work in the late 1840s. Mays Hill Pit was an
upcast, with Guibal fan; later a Capell fan was also installed. The very early Nibley shaft was used for
pumping. Frog Lane also had a large Cornish pump made by J & E Bush of Bristol, with a $85\frac{1}{2}$ in
cylinder with a 10 ft stroke. Working at 6 strokes per minute the engine could raise 503,000 gallons of
water in 10 hours. This engine was disused by World War II.

Only two seams were worked at Frog Lane Colliery in the 96 years of working; the Hard Seam which
was 2 ft 6 ins thick, and the High Seam which was 4 ft 3 ins in section. As the Hard and High Seams were
nearing exhaustion it was decided to try and work an area of the Hollybush Vein in 1944. Two headings
commenced in disturbed ground, and the development was pursued with the hope that conditions would
improve, but the two panels encountered rolls in the coal and they were abandoned in 1947. When the
other two seams were totally exhausted the colliery closed in 1949.

The workforce at Nationalisation stood at 258 underground workers who produced about 3,500 tons
of coal per month.

Frog Lane Colliery's motive power was *Lord Salisbury,* an inside six cylinder six coupled Peckett
locomotive, which was built in 1906 for the Coalpit Heath Co. The locomotive had 16 inch cylinders;

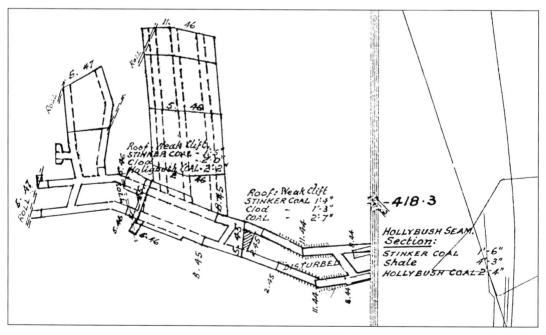

The Colliery abandonment plan of 1949, showing the last attempt to work the Hollybush Seam. Note the rolls
and weak roof which sealed the fate of the colliery.

when the colliery closed it was moved to Norton Hill Colliery in 1950 but was unfortunately scrapped by a dealer in Trowbridge in 1965.

The only remaining structure of Coalpit Heath Colliery is the engine house of the horizontal winding engine which has lost its roof, and Rock house (? the offices or manager's house) and some workshops.

An early photograph of Coalpit Heath Colliery with the manager Francis Eames in white coat in timber yard around 1910. This colliery remained unchanged until closure by the National Coal Board in 1949,

HARRY STOKE MINE, STOKE GIFFORD, BRISTOL

6

Speedwell Colliery was abandoned in 1936. The Kingswood Great Vein was the main seam worked but with the working faces around one mile inbye from the pit bottom the accessible reserves were exhausted.

In the 1950s the newly established National Coal Board drew up plans to open up the northern area of the coalfield just one mile to the north of the abandoned workings of Speedwell Colliery. This post-Nationalisation venture was located on Triassic deposits in which a pair of drifts was driven through the Triassic beds at a gradient of 1 in 3.3 into the coal measures along their natural dip.

A number of bore holes were put down at Harry Stoke and Downend to prove the seams of the Middle Series. It was originally intended that a flank face should be worked from the dip development for a distance of 1,500 ft. Then new drifts were to be driven 3,000 ft along the crop and these again to extract 1,500 ft on either side, and then yet another drift mine for the next 3,000 ft panel. As the drift mines reached the deeper measures shafts were to be sunk beyond to extend the extraction of coal. The Board also had plans to sink a large modern style colliery in the Downend area, to link with the Harry Stoke Mine and other planned drifts, but this project was soon abandoned.

Three seams were accessible from the new drift, the Five Coals , Great Vein, and Gillers Inn. The Five Coals and Gillers Inn Seam are about 100 feet apart with the Kingswood Great Vein intervening. The upper seam, the Five Coals, was the most extensively worked, and was the best seam to work. Panels were set off north and south from the drifts, but each stopped due to disturbance, some times in the form of barren ground and sometimes thin coal. The northern varied from 300 ft to 1,200 ft, each successive panel advancing further than the previous one.

In 1959, the pit made a profit of 1s. 6d. per ton amounting to £9,200. This was achieved by four good months January, February, March and April with a cumulative profit of £21,400, but in the succeeding months £12,000 was dissipated by increasing losses month by month.

After 1959, working in the Five Coals Seam was gradually reduced due to faulting and in spite of prolonged exploration it was not possible to find the extent of the fault, or the continuity of the seam. It was then decided to abandon it and that the Great Vein and Gillers Inn Vein be developed. A 420 ft orthodox machine-cut hand-got face was opened in the Great Vein but was soon abandoned due to thin section and barren ground; the face only yielded 80 tons of coal.

A 480 ft plough face was prepared in the Gillers Inn Seam in 1961, but due to a friable roof and fluctuations of 12 to 15in. in the seam section, the output was low and the quality very poor. The Gillers Inn seam had to be worked by hand, as attempts to power load failed. These faces encountered disturbances and the seven faces worked in the seam did not achieve the advances that the Five Coals Faces did.

After the abandonment of the Five Coals Seam and Kingswood Great Vein the main face was the M7 face in the Gillers Inn Seam. 180 ft from the right hand gate, barren ground appeared to affect the face for some 111 ft. Another face, the N9 face was 270 ft long with a section of 4 ft 8 ins but had the Five Feet fault crossing the face from left to right. Production on this face was limited due the inability of the gate belt to carry coal up the gradient.

Recently discovered papers, thought to date from late 1962 or early in 1963, show that the mine had produced 470,000 tons of coal with a total loss of £818,900 or 35s. per ton overall. In 1962 the mine produced a loss of 14s. 6d. per ton and total loss of £50,000.

NUM documents suggest that insufficient effort had been made to penetrate the disturbances and that the emphasis had been to maintain an output of 300 tons at all cost, with a result that new faces were opened without sufficient effort having been made to re-establish the old ones. The Board replied by saying that it did not appear that continuing successful operation could be anticipated within the horizons as yet worked, and if the mine were to become economic it must extend further into the to coal measures. NCB engineers felt that there was no indication that the deeper measures would be better, and secondly the strata dipped over at the extremity of the drift, so conveying and working wiuld become more difficult.

Saleable output in 1960 was 65,927 tons, with a loss of £48,200, the last quarter having made a loss of £21,000. The reserves at June 1961 were said to be 200,000 tons, and the Board said that to extract the coal, extensive exploration and drivage would have been needed.

Bore hole data held by the Coal Board indicated that disturbed conditions continued and the seams might well deteriorate further. The greater depth would entail the sinking of a ventilation shaft and increased transport facilities would be required. The Board also felt it could not feel justified in risking the throwing of so much more good money after bad.

A letter from the Chairman of the NCB stated that the friable roof conditions (which made mechanisation almost impossible), and the high ash content which was 30 per cent, were no longer acceptable to the Central Electrical Generating Board for their modern design of power station furnaces, so the possibility of working these two seams offered no hope of producing a more marketable product. From the production and marketing viewpoint therefore the Board came to the conclusion that they must accept the Divisional Board's recommendation that the colliery must close.

The colliery employed just under 190 men of which 40 were employed on salvage work for about 3 months, and 40 were offered immediate employment at other pits in Somerset. The rest of the men who were willing to move were offered employment elsewhere in the South Western Division, with the full benefits of the Board transfer scheme. The men who were over 60 received an immediate pension under the Mineworkers' Pension Scheme, in addition to redundancy compensation.

Production 1954-63

	Manpower	Saleable Output Tons
1954	*107*	4,430
1955	*160*	12, 996
1956	*178*	42,380
1957	*276*	46,507
1958	*299*	71,125
1959	not known	101,000
1960	not known	not known
1961	*211*	47.025
1962	*206*	65,900
1963	*174*	16,076

Closure 14 June

Elevated tub line from drift entrance to screens and washery.

The screens and loading bays in 1960.

Muir Hill dumper tuck carrying spoil to waste tip, 1960.

The commencement of the Harry Stoke Drift Mine project in the early 1950s. This is the No.1 drift looking south; the electric pylon is still standing today. Photograph by Ray Ashman.

Above: The entrance to the No.2 drift uncovered in the landscaping of
the site for the Ministry of Defence in the 1990s.

Opposite page: Road to old workings with temporary stopping.

Transfer point at bottom of drift with loaded mine car, May 1961.

Full mine cars waiting at the bottom of drift before being wound to surface.

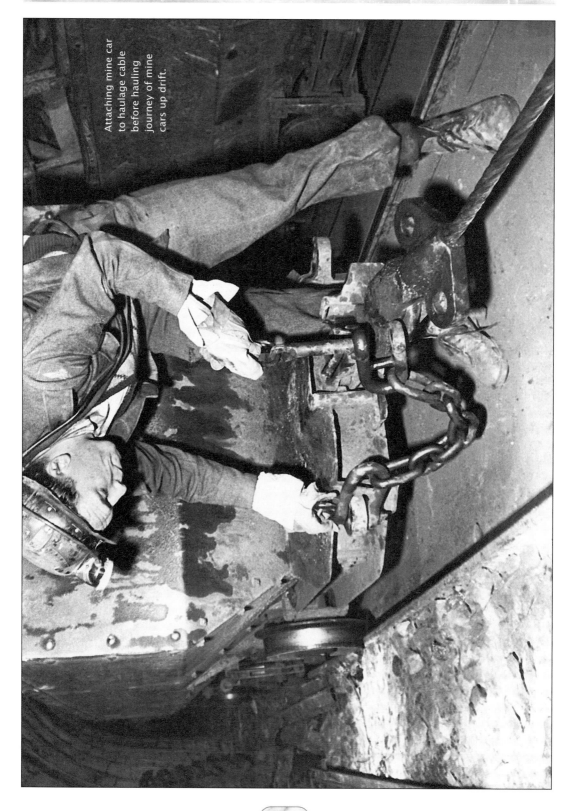

Attaching mine car to haulage cable before hauling journey of mine cars up drift.

KILMERSDON & WRITHLINGTON COLLIERIES, RADSTOCK, SOMERSET

7

Writhlington Colliery was the first pit in this complex to be sunk in 1829. The coaling shaft was originally sunk to a depth of 394 ft with a diameter of 10 ft. Prior to 1900 the shaft was deepened to a depth of 1,461 ft. The main coaling shaft of Kilmersdon Colliery was commenced in February 1874 and was 858 ft deep by 1877, as was the second or pumping shaft. The main shaft was also later deepened to 1,560 ft. Both Kilmersdon and Writhlington Collieries were on land owned by Lord Hilton who granted the leases.

At the commencement of working at Kilmersdon & Writhlington Collieries, all coal was won by undercutting with a pick and was loaded by hand into "putts" and removed by carting boys using a "guss and crook" to main roadways where tubs were filled and taken by horses to the pit bottoms.

The Writhlington Coal Co. acquired Kilmersdon Colliery in 1928. Soon after, the first conveyor face was introduced to improve the output. After World War II and Nationalisation in 1947, plans were drawn up to modernise the coalfield and mechanise the thin seams. In the mid-1950s, a face at Writhlington Colliery in the No.5 Seam, in the Longs district, was found to be 480 ft long, in double units each 240 ft in length. The coal was cut at floor level using an A.B. 12 ins - 40 H.P. machine, which was known to cut into the fireclay floor. The face was wet cut and the coal was hand filled onto a 20 ins bottom belt conveyor. In good conditions 240 ft of coal could be cut in one shift. To achieve a daily output of approximately 150 tons, 51 men were employed.

When coal winding ceased at Foxcote Colliery in 1931, Writhlington was the only remaining pit in the area. The Rock vein and the No.5 seams, around 2 ft 6 ins and 20 ins thick, were the main source of output from Writhlington and the old Foxcote take, now being worked from Writhlington. In 1960 a connection had been made into the 4 ft thick No.10 seam which was worked from Kilmersdon Colliery.

Prior the Nationalisation of the industry in 1947, the lower part of the Kilmersdon Upcast and pumping shaft collapsed, and this stopped all production at the pit for six months. A connection was made between Writhlington and the No.5 seam, and Writhlington became the downcast shaft and Kilmersdon winding shaft the upcast.

It was proposed that a German machine known as an Eickhoff Hydraulic SE11 cutter, which would cost £3,000, but fitted with British electric drives, would be acquired with a static plough also by Eickhoff. The cutter was to be fitted with double horizontal jibs; the bottom jib to be used for dealing with bottom coal. This machinery would operate with a prop-free front, but would need props to be set on the face side immediately behind the cutting and loading operations. Only 29 men would be required as opposed to 51 men for the conventional Somerset method. The Trepanner had been found to be unsuitable because of its narrow web, the depth of the cut of the machine and the problems of handling heavy cable in low seams.

By 1961 all coal faces in both pits were mechanised with the German ploughs, and armoured face chain conveyors, with British hydraulic props, replacing wooden and steel supports. The hydraulic props were later replaced by fully automatic hydraulic self advancing chocks, and rubber conveyor belts in the roads carrying the coal to the pit bottoms.

By 1967 Kilmersdon/Writhlington produced its highest tonnage of saleable coal, 280,000, which was 1,135 tons per working day. The workforce was 670 men, but the working faces were over two miles inbye from the shaft bottom. As the workings were extended outwards the quality of the coal had deteriorated with an increasing ash content, so coal from the Midlands had to be blended in with it.

In 1973, the year the colliery ceased working, the K14 working face was served by a 26 in. wide conveyor of 30 h.p. There was also a Huwood Twin Conveyor Twin chain conveyor with a capacity of 100 tons. The Kilmersdon shaft worked at 30 winds per hour, 90 trams of coal were wound in an hour, and this came to a total of 85 tons an hour.

The steam winding engine at Kilmersdon was replaced by an electric winder from Scotland in 1963. Following the closure of Norton Hill Colliery in 1966, the electric winder from that colliery was installed at Writhlington to replace the last steam winding engine in Somerset in regular use. Two battery locomotives from Norton Hill were installed underground to carry men over one mile to and from the working faces. These faces had been previously equipped with plough, hydraulic roof supports (or chocks) and chain conveyors. Coal which was produced at Writhlington was raised there until closure, while the men used the baths at Kilmersdon and the baths at the closed Ludlows Pit. Kilmersdon Colliery had a three deck cage, each deck holding one tub of 19cwts of coal, Writhlington Colliery had a two deck cage, also carrying one tub in each deck. At the time of closure, the faces were up to three miles from the Kilmersdon shaft and two miles from the pit bottom of Writhlington shaft.

The surface buildings at Kilmersdon Colliery were built of the local Lias stone and were laid out with the two shafts on an east-west line. The bottom section of the steel headframe over the coaling shaft was enclosed in a low single storey structure covering the pit bank and area surrounding the shaft. The small headframe on the emergency shaft, which was formerly the pumping shaft, was located in the open on the eastern side of the pithead to the north of the Cornish engine house. Unfortunately, no details of the pumping engine are now available.

The two winding engine houses were situated east and west of the shafts and were also built of the local Lias stone which had been dressed with highly decorated facia boards. The remaining buildings on the site were mainly built with sheets asbestos on steel frames, as were the baths and offices and were of no particular merit, unlike the original buildings.

The original buildings of Writhlington Colliery were also built of local Lias stone with the shafts laid out on an east-west line with the coaling shaft situated on the west, and the Cornish pumping engine and shaft on the east. The pumping engine house was pulled down in 1960. The large winding house for the horizontal winder was also demolished in 1966 and replaced by an electric winder.

The unusual feature of Writhlington Colliery was the public road which ran between the winding engine and the pithead. The only other known similar arrangement was Crown Colliery at Warmley, Bristol.

Apart from the pithead structure and workshop most of the buildings were replaced by steel framed asbestos clad structures, so that when closure came in 1973, little remained of the original Victorian pit except for the lattice headframe and pit head.

Some little-known facts are that Kilmersdon/Writhlington colliery recorded the lowest accident rate in the Somerset and South Wales area to which it was attached. This colliery also recorded the lowest absentee percentage rates in the whole of the British Mining Industry, and was well known for its good record of being dispute free, and its outstanding men/management relationships. This is despite of the fact that the Bristol and Somerset Coalfield was very difficult to work, because of the complex geological structure which was due the nearness of the Mendip Hills. The area contains extremely severe faulting and disturbances and it was surprising that the coalfield kept workings into the 1970s. It has been said many times that a Somerset miner could work anywhere.

THE KILMERSDON COLLIERY SELF ACTING INCLINE

The sinking of the main coaling shaft of Kilmersdon Colliery began in 1874 and the first coal was wound in 1878. It appears that the incline was constructed in the previous year. A comparison today with the 1883 25 inch Ordnance Survey map shows the incline had changed little over the 90 years before closure. The only alteration was additional tipping on the southern side of the incline and further sidings to the northern.

The working of the incline was a simple operation. A full standard 16 ton wagon descended the northern track of the incline, pulling an empty wagon up on the southern track. These wagons were controlled by two brake levers between the tracks, which acted on brake bands on the two horizontal cable drums in the winding house at the head of the incline. Two stops were placed at the head of the incline to prevent wagons from accidentally plunging over the edge.

The Kilmersdon Incline was the last gravity operated incline in the country.

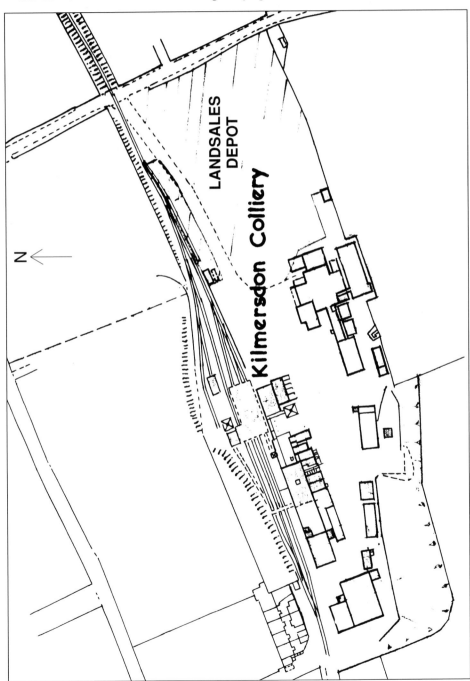

The surface layout of Kilmersdon Colliery in the 1970s. The baths situated in the south eastern corner of the site, with the main pithead ranged along the south side of the railway track.

General View of Kilmersdon Colliery taken from the south in 1972. The baths are in the foreground with the two winding engine houses east and west of the main headframe, with the engine house of the Cornish pump in front of the headframe.

The Pit Head in 1972 with the empty Cornish engine house in front of the second shaft's smaller headframe.

The interior of the pithead with three deck cage and clapper board on left of cage. (see opposite page).

Close-up of clapper boards; these boards were the last in Somerset and the only others were in use at Fernhill Colliery in the Rhondda Valley and were disused by 1980. The purpose of these boards was to prevent atmospheric air from leaking into the upcast shaft.

Above: The platform of the small cage, this was the original pumping shaft.

Opposite page: The headframe of the smaller second shaft. This was the original pumping shaft, but became an upcast. The original shear legs of the Cornish Pump can just be seen behind the steel headframe. The cage could carry two men.

Surface worker on picking belt.

The screens in 1968-9 with Vic Sage on the right, the man on the left is thought to be a surface foreman. This belt produced hand picked coal for the domestic market.

Cecil Jones operating the brake on the gravity operated incline 1971. This and an incline at Whitehaven were the last of the gravity operated inclines to work in the country.

The bottom or northern part of the incline taken from the ex-GWR line. A full wagon is about to be lowered and an empty wagon is set to rise. The speed being regulated by a brake on the drum in a house at the head of the incline.

The 0-4-0 Peckett locomotive built in Bristol in 1929. This engine worked full wagons to the head of the incline and returned empty ones back to the screens.

Harry Loader the driver of the Peckett
0-40 engine on the head of the incline,
1971. Herb, as he was known, was one of
the last drivers on the Peckett locomotive.
Note the bore holes which were put down
after the Aberfan Disaster to check on the
water content of the tip, over which
the railway track and incline were laid.

Above: The last tram raised at Kilmersdon Colliery in 1974,
with names of the last workforce. 25 July 1974.

Below: The boilerhouse and chimney taken in 1961 by Nigel Booth .

The cutting disk of a Dawson Miller machine in 1961; this was a forerunner of the longwall shearer which is now standard longwall equipment. This machine was not successful and was phased out in the early 1960s.

Submersible pumps which had been withdrawn from the No 2 shaft in July 1974.

Writhington Colliery taken in 1968. This was the most attractive setting of any Somerset Colliery set on the old Somerset and Dorset Railway. The fine old winding and pumping engines houses have been removed and a new steel and asbestos structure now houses the electric winding engine.

Writhlington Colliery in 1973 from the south, the tree-covered tip on the hill belonging to Braysdown Colliery.

The pithead building and fine lattice headframe taken in 1968. Note the dark blue lorry in the current NCB livery, under the rubbish bunker, the conveyor was connected to the tippler shown on page 56. A public road (shown here) ran under the winding rope between the engine house and pithead.

Above: The pithead and headframe in 1972 .

Opposite page; Top: The interior of the pithead with tippler in 1968.

*Opposite page; Below:*The wooden guides on the top of the shaft.

Looking down the Writhington shaft with its wooden guides and pit work.

A plough and armoured conveyor, on the face at Writhlington Colliery May 1961. Nigel Booth.

A plough at the gate end of the face, the plough is mounted on the armoured conveyer and driven by an electric motor on the end of the face. Writhlington Colliery May 1961. Nigel Booth.

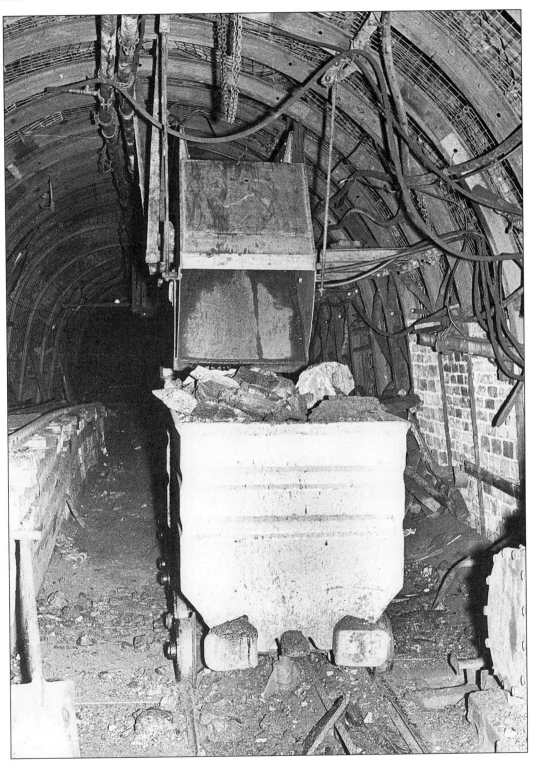

Writhlington Colliery, pit bottom loading point with ramp from creeper, June 1960. (Nigel Booth)

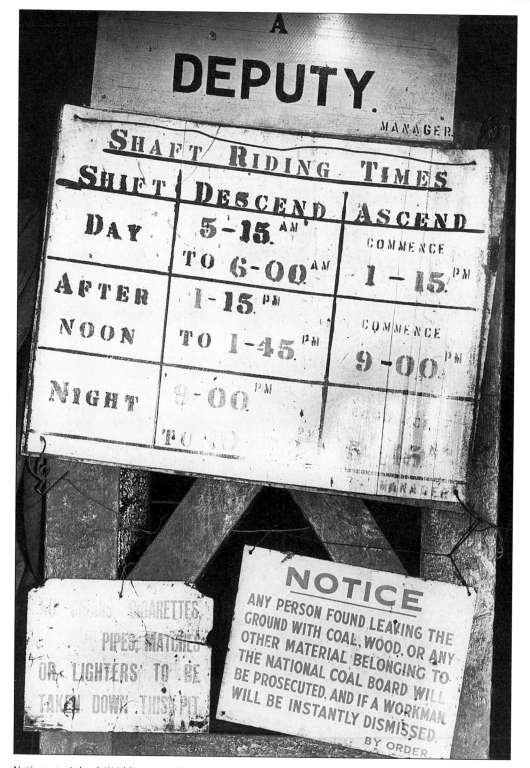

Notices at pit bank Writhlington Colliery.

The cutting disk of the Dawson Miller machine on a face at Writhlington, May 1961. This machine was not successful and was soon withdrawn. (Nigel Booth)

Frank Day setting up a Dowty hydraulic prop on a Writhlington face in 1961. (Nigel Booth)

A transfer point in Writhlington Colliery in 1961. (Nigel Booth)

Controls for plough face at Writhlington Colliery. (Nigel Booth)

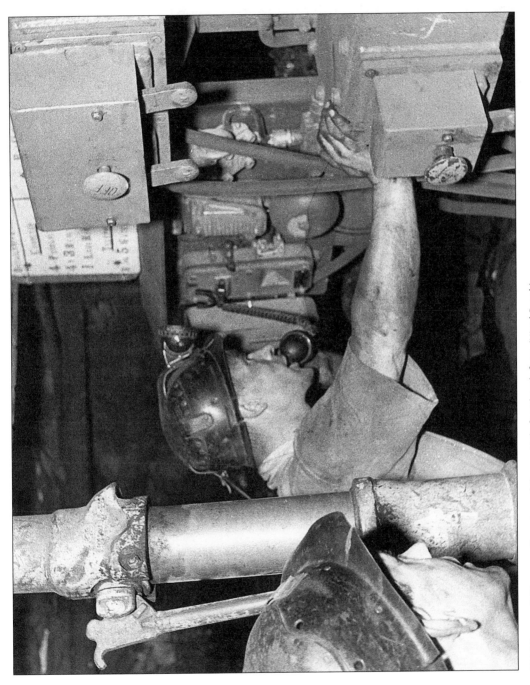

Writhlington Colliery, another view of the controls for plough face. (Nigel Booth)

Writhlington Colliery road leading to plough face; taken in 1960. (Nigel Booth)

Writhlington Collieries washery, 1968.

Writhlington Colliery 1968. Coal bunkers and rail loading point, the weigh-bridge is on the extreme right.

Writhlington Colliery, January 1961. The original steam winding house and stump of the Cornish pump house and chimney.

Demolition of Writhlington Colliery in 1974.

LUDLOWS COLLIERY, RADSTOCK, SOMERSET

Ludlows Colliery was certainly one of the three earliest pits to be sunk in Radstock It was at work in the late 1790s and was shown on an estate map of 1806 to be an extensive undertaking on the surface, with a large structure which appeared to contain a large haystack boiler. The winding shaft of Ludlows Colliery was an upcast originally with a diameter of 4 ft 6 ins, later widened to 8 ft. The depth was 1,695 ft including the sump of 30 ft. This shaft was sunk in badly disturbed ground and passed through the same seam three times. The second or later winding engine was in 1890 a single horizontal cylinder of 36 ins with a 5 ft stroke working with high pressure steam. Two tubs were carried on each cage with two decks. By the 1890s the Radstock seams were mainly worked out but the Farrington seams were in the process of being opened out.

The haulage engine, which was placed on the surface, was a beam engine with a single cylinder of 26 ins diameter geared 1 to 2 with one drum formerly used for winding (presumably on the second shaft, the presence of which has now been confirmed). This engine conveyed six sets of tubs over a dip plane, the top of which was close to the bottom of the shaft. The length of the plane was 2,400 ft with a dip of 6 ins to the yard.

The colliery take was large as was to be expected of a pit which had been working for 150 years. It was linked to the Wells Way Pit and a quantity of the Wells Way coal was raised at Ludlows. The pit was also linked to Braysdown Colliery, and also worked northwards until the workings were only 600 ft south of the Clandown shafts.

By the time of Nationalisation it had been working for about 150 years, and was nearing exhaustion, and played little part in the plans of the National Coal Board in Somerset. A document of 1949 stated that it was unlikely that the pit would ever be worked economically, and it was being retained solely to find work for the men. What a different place was the world in the late 1940s: there was a good side to the old NCB.

The colliery had a saleable output of 50,861 tons in 1947, 53,320 tons in 1948, but the output had dropped to 47,885 tons in 1949 and 43,965 tons in 1950.

The NCB closed the colliery on 19 March 1954, although the baths were used by the men from Writhlington Colliery until that pit closed in 1973.

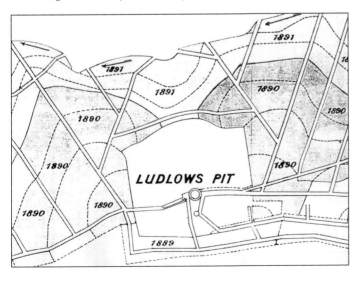

Ludlows Colliery plan of the late 1890s showing the second shaft.

Ludlows Colliery some time before Nationalisation. Today only the chimney and headframe are missing; most pit buildings are still standing.

Engine house for a beam engine used on second shaft for moving tubs on
a dip plane near the pit bottom. Taken in the 1960s.

The early history of the colliery is obscure. It dates from the early 1820s, but little or no mining information exists apart from the shaft section published in *Buckland & Conybeare* of 1824, of the Chilcompton New Pit. This is highly likely to be New Rock Colliery, and covers the Small Coal Seam, Two Coal Seam and Warkey Course.

By 1870 New Rock Pit is recorded as working the following seams:

The Globe seam	*3ft 0in*
Small Coal	*1ft 6in*
Two Coal	*1ft 8in*
Warkey Seam	*2ft 6in*
Garden Course	*3ft 6in*

The Globe Seam had been followed at New Rock to a depth of 900 ft and the Garden Course Seam was wrought from the bottom of the new shaft 1,200 ft in depth by 1870.

The two shafts at New Rock Colliery were said to be 4 ft 6 ins in diameter, the depth varied in different documents and is either 1,117 ft or 1,182 ft in depth. The downcast shaft was the main coaling shaft and the upcast shaft was the pumping shaft situated further the east. The main shaft originally had a beam winding engine with a 31 ins cylinder, 6 ft stroke, and was geared 1 to 3. The drum was plain with a diameter of 12 ft. This engine wound a three deck cage which carried three tubs of 10 cwt each. The guides were wood and the rope was not counterbalanced in any way. The second steam winder was of an unknown make, but thought have been brought to the pit around 1903. This winding engine had a small 8 ft diameter drum, twin cylinders 26 ins in diameter with a 5 ft stroke. The engine wound three tubs each carrying ten cwt (as above). An unusual feature is the very small diameter of the shaft and the fact that the whole load is completely dead and unbalanced. This small engine had to raise the cage and coal tubs, plus the steel rope unaided, as did the first engine.

A first pumping engine, which was of the Cornish Type, was made by Winwood of Bristol and was erected in 1824. The engine had a 50 ins cylinder and a 7 ft 6 in stroke and worked day and night raising water in three lifts from a depth of 180 yards. The engine delivered 180 gallons of water per minute to the surface.

The early ventilation of the colliery was created by a water-fall in the downcast shaft, as far as the Globe seam. The quantity of air in circulation was 3,000 cubic feet and this was thought sufficient to carry off the carbonic acid gas which infested the mine. No firedamp was produced and naked lights were used.

The winding shaft of New Rock Colliery was originally sunk to the Globe Vein, 546 ft deep, as was the pumping shaft, but a shaft section held by Bristol Coalmining Archives Ltd shows the winding shaft to be sunk to the Garden Course Seam, at a depth of 1,182 ft. The pumping shaft terminated at the Globe Vein with a staple (or internal) pit sunk to the Small Coal Vein at a depth of 878 ft.

A steep incline was driven from the shaft bottom with a gradient of 1 in 2 into the Great Course Seam. A compressed air haulage engine was situated at the head of the incline. This layout proved to be the limiting factor in the expansion plans for the colliery, which later resulted in the reopening of the old Strap Pit.

The geology at New Rock Colliery was certainly different from the main Somerset pits; the seams were thicker in section, although the Small Coal Seam or New Seam varied considerably. They were all extremely steep, and some faulted, but the reserves were considerable: many millions of tons.

In the early 1950s the NCB needed to increase the output in Somerset and particularly New Rock Colliery which had good reserves, but was restricted by the deep but small diameter shaft. It was decided to drain and investigate the Strap Pit near Stratton-on-the-Fosse, to assess the possibility of reopening it, and working the extensive reserves of coal in the mainly virgin Lower Series of seams. In the winter of 1954-55 a temporary headframe and winding gear were erected and a 250 h.p. submersible pump was installed. This was capable of lifting nearly 2 million gallons of water out of the shaft in a week, and pumping was carried out day and night to dewater the 1,834 ft deep shaft, which took 18 months to accomplish.

One of the objects of reopening the shaft was to determine the positions of the seams in the shaft, but the shaft was found to be completely lined with brick, and unfortunately no markers were found to indicate the seam positions.

Once the 10 feet diameter shaft had been drained and new permanent headframe and winding engine had been installed, a 3,000 ft roadway was driven through to New Rock Colliery from the now renamed Mendip Colliery. This new roadway also provided an alternative means of access and adequate ventilation. A new 1,500 ft trunk conveyor was installed to carry the output direct to the pit bottom siding which were constructed at the bottom of the Mendip shaft where the coal was loaded into mine cars.

Coal was first raised on the 23 December 1963. Ploughs had been installed on the faces, but were found to be unsuitable in the thick steep seams. So after only four years of working the NCB drew up plans to close New Rock Colliery which ceased working on the 28 September 1968, leaving a vast amount of unworked coal.

Apart from the offices, now a dwelling, nothing remains of the colliery, except for the tip. The winding house still stands at Mendip Colliery as does the weighbridge house, now Jacksons Timber yard.

General view of New Rock Colliery winding shaft. In 1966 the winding was still carried out by a steam winder, which was replaced by an electric winder just before the colliery closed. The stump of a building on the right of the picture is possibly the remains of the original beam winding engine house.

The headframe on the pumping shaft which became the second or
emergency shaft and was also the upcast shaft.

The New Rock colliery yard in October 1960. The large building on the right was the electricity station, the headframe of the upcast shaft can just be seen on the left. Nigel Booth.

The remains of the Lancashire boilers and upcast shaft with the power house in the background in 1967.

The headframe over the Strap Pit, later known as Mendip Colliery, in 1961 with the original buildings of Strap Pit on either side of the shaft. (Nigel Booth)

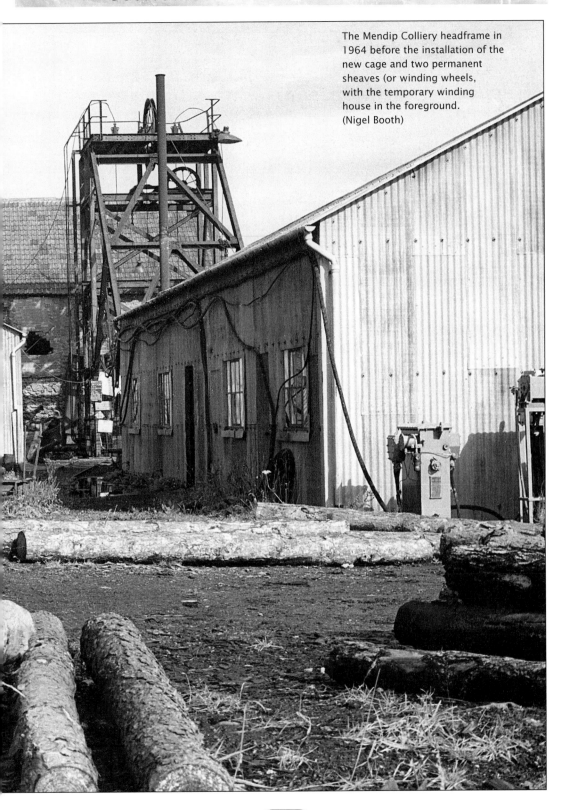

The Mendip Colliery headframe in
1964 before the installation of the
new cage and two permanent
sheaves (or winding wheels,
with the temporary winding
house in the foreground.
(Nigel Booth)

The pit bank of the Mendip shaft in 1962. Note the kibble used by the shaftsmen (far left). (Nigel Booth)

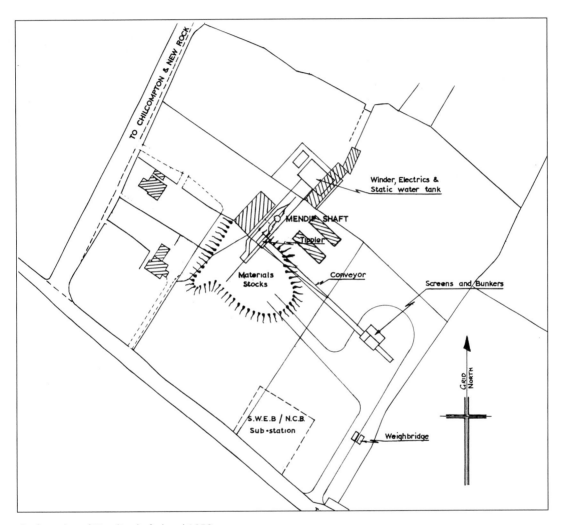

Surface plan of Mendip shaft dated 1958.

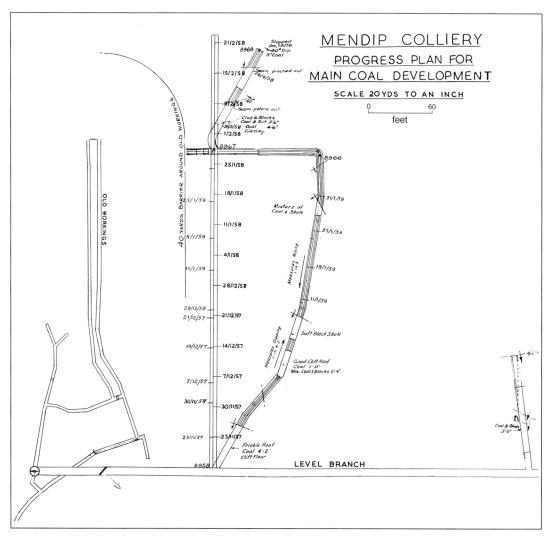

Underground plan of Mendip shaft dated 1957, showing old workings abandoned and reused old roads, with dates of new drivage.

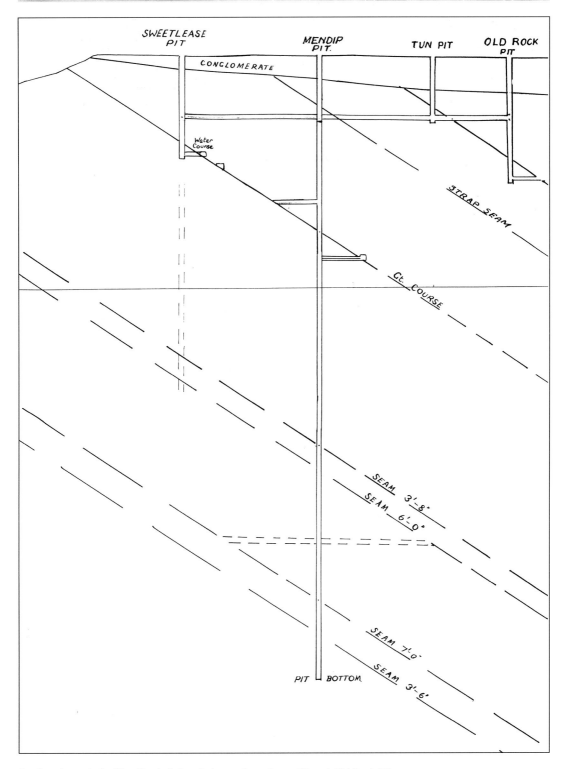

Section through the Mendip shaft in relation to Sweetlease Pit and Old Rock Pits.

The original Old Norton Hill pit was sunk some time in the late 1840s or early 1850s. A pair of small 4 ft diameter shafts were sunk, but did not work long before being abandoned, and left waterlogged. In 1897 the Beauchamp family acquired the pit and began dewatering it; they had succeeded in doing so by 1899. It is not clear what happened to the original pumping engine; it is highly likely that the engine was disposed of when the pit was abandoned. The Old Norton Hill pit was not intended for raising coal but was to be used for ventilation and a second means of escape.

In 1902 sinking had begun on the shaft of Norton Hill (new) Pit which was originally sunk to a depth of 1,500 ft in brick, and was 13 ft in diameter. This pit was sunk alongside the Somerset & Dorset Railway and it was connected to the main line by a siding around 1903.

At the start of World War II an underground connection was made into the deep shaft of Old Welton Colliery which was reopened, and used for ventilation and as a third means of escape with the two shafts Old Norton and New Pit. The seams worked at Norton Hill varied in thickness from 22 ins to 4 ft 6 ins, but were all subject to geological faults.

When operated under the National Coal Board the winding at Old Welton Pit was undertaken by a portable steam engine, until replaced by electric winding gear.

A survey made at the time of Nationalisation showed that the pit had suffered from lack of investment during and after World War II, but this was the case with most pits then. The pit was still operating as sunk, with ever-extending tub tracks and large number of underground haulage engines, and no conveyors. Even so, the colliery still made a profit; indeed it was the only Somerset pit to do so. A press release of 1949 stated the pit would have a life of more than 20 years, but no further reserves were available from the present shafts.

In the early 1950s a scheme for reconstructing Norton Hill Colliery, then in the South Western Division of the National Coal Board, was approved and £500,000 was granted to complete the work. The system chosen was in operation at the Llanharn Mine in Glamorgan and it was planned to operate Norton Hill along the same lines with local modifications, to work 6,000,000 tons of coal. The reconstruction of this naked light pit was hoped to be completed in four years. The project entailed the enlarging and straightening of existing roadways, and the driving of a complete new 1,800 ft cross measure roadway which intersected four seams, which were worked, the Nos. 5, 6, 7 and 10 seams. Production was first concentrated mainly in the No. 6 and 10 seams. A roadway was driven from the No. 10 seam into the No. 11 which first produced 60 tons a day. The colliery also worked towards the Old Welton area where there were large reserves in the No. 5, 6, 7 and 10 seams which were supposed to give the pit an extensive life.

Over the next five years coal was worked with modern ploughs on the longwall system, with shaker conveyors and belt conveyors in all gates, electrically driven. All surface plant was electrified including the steam winding engine, and winders at the Old Norton Pit and Old Welton Pit. Almost all of the surface was renewed, the new surface layout included concreting a large part of the colliery yard.

Production had stood at 160,000 tons per annum in 1949 and the output per man shift at the coalface was 33.7 cwts. Production was expected to expand gradually until 1954, when there should have been an annual output of 250,000 tons. or 43.3 cwts per man-shift. A labour force of 700 men was employed in 1949, and it was hoped to build up the numbers to 850 by the end of 1951.

A number of ten-ton 50 h.p. battery locomotives were in use by 1951 and these worked underground for around ten years, on the bottom level on the south side. The locomotives pulled journeys of 45 tubs with a net load of 33 tons. Eventually they were sent to Kilmersdon Colliery.

A new 2,520 ft conveyor belt was installed in 1962 and immediately increased the flow of coal to the pit bottom. This resulted in the colliery making profits again, but unfortunately within several years the manpower shortage forced the pit into single shift working and with severe geological problems losses mounted, and the pit was forced into closure in 1966.

Norton Hill Colliery before modernisation, the wooden headframe was soon replaced with a steel structure and a new engine house was built to house the electric winder. Taken by Ray Ashman.

Miners at the Pit Bottom, Norton Hill Colliery, mid 1950s. From left tp right: Jack Haggett, Unknown, Arthur Davidson, Maurice the Pole, Alb Taylor, Cliff Hitchens and John Paget.

Greenwood & Batley underground electric locomotive with Jack Haggett,
Norton Hill Colliery, 1950s.

The pit head area in 1961 with tubs of supplies on the creeper, with new steel rings in foreground.

Lord Salisbury, a Peckett 0-6-0 locomotive, working at Norton Hill in the 1950s. This engine had worked at Frog Lane Colliery, Coalpit Heath until 1949, and was then moved to Norton Hill where the engine worked until closure in 1965. Photograph by Ray Ashman.

Marsh Lane was the smallest of the Somerset Collieries to be taken into the ownership of the National Coal Board in 1947.

The mine was begun after 1921 when the old Farrington Pit was closed. In the following years of depression and unemployment, a number of unemployed miners applied to the Duchy of Cornwall who gave permission open a new seam. Two drifts were sunk on land at Marsh Lane situated to the east of Rush Hill, Farrington Gurney, and miners were allowed to draw their dole until they struck coal. Other pit workers joined the original 17 men, and the colliery eventually opened the 21 Inch seam in 1924. In the general strike of 1926 the colliery was unique, as it was allowed to carry on working while the other pits were idle.

The colliery take was bounded on the north by a major fault known as the Winterfield Fault, and to the west the workings extended to within 100 feet of the coal crop of the No.10 vein. A barrier of coal 200 feet wide was left to the east of the take; this barrier separated Marsh Lane workings from the old workings of Farrington Colliery.

The No. 10 Vein is in two sections at Farrington, one known as the Bantam Vein 2 ft thick and other the Stony Vein which is thin. There is a third seam the Night Vein 12 ins thick above the Bantam, which was not worked at Marsh Lane Drift.

When the 21 Inch seam was nearing exhaustion it was decided to drive a branch to locate a new seam, the Rudge, 2ft 4in to 2ft 9in thick. This seam was struck in February a month after Nationalisation. 35 men were employed at Marsh Lane, which in 1948 produced a saleable output of 6,097 tons p.a., of coal. The output was about 120 tons per week in 1949, an output of 14 cwt per man shift which compared well with other collieries. The output per man shift dropped to 12.6 cwt in the 3 months before closure, which the National Coal Board said was caused by a persistent loss averaging 10s.6d per ton of coal worked.

The men were assured that they would be given jobs at Old Mills Colliery, a model pit nearby, and they were told that their wages would remain unchanged, but according to a local newspaper, the Marsh Lane men were said to be doubtful. The men also claimed that the coal they produced was acknowledged as some of the best in Somerset and could continue for many years, since the Rudge seam had reserves of 2,000,000 tons. The NCB officials claimed that there was only one third of that amount of coal, but the Marsh Lane miners stated that no Coal Board official had ever seen the seam.

The plan of the workings of Marsh Lane colliery show that most of the available reserves had been worked out, so the Coal Board had the last say and closed the drift on the 5 November 1949.

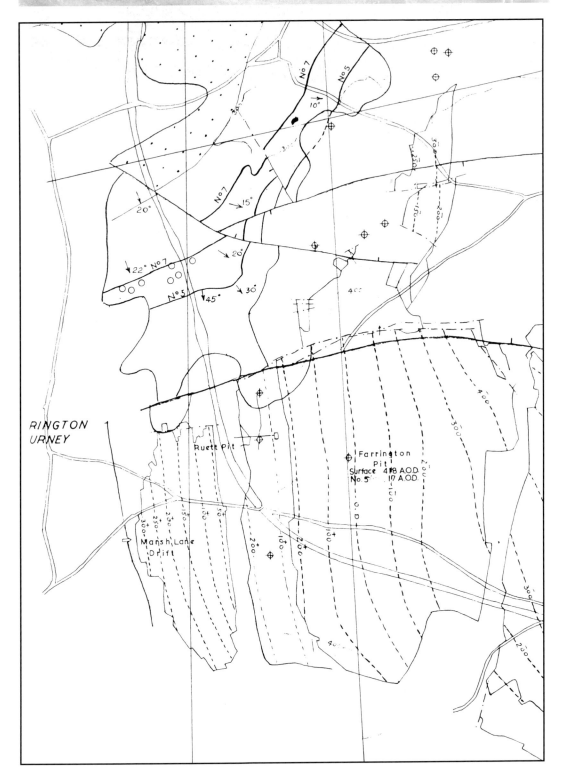

Although owned by the same company there were the two pits worked as separate collieries until Nationalisation in 1947. Old Mills, the northernmost pit, was the first to be sunk in around 1860; the date 1861 was cast into the frame of the winding engine at Old Mills Colliery. The second pit known as Springfield Colliery was sunk later. The date of 1868 was present on the wooden headframe which does suggest that shaft sinking had commenced some time before then.

The colliery take was bounded on the north by the Winterfield fault, although three panels had been worked to the north of the fault. To the south, the three seams were worked almost to the concealed outcrops. The workings of Norton Hill Colliery and the old workings of Farrington Pit were present on the east and west side of the take.

There was a 200 feet barrier of unworked coal between Old Mills Colliery and the old Farrington Pit to the west. The eastern boundary terminated at Providence Place and North Road in Midsomer Norton, with only a 100 feet barrier of unworked coal between the No.5 and No.7 seams of Old Mills and Norton Hill Colliery.

The Springfield shaft had a diameter of 10 ft and was the downcast and winding shaft. The pit bottom was in the Bottom Vein 960 ft from the surface. The Old Mills shaft was used as the upcast, and was 10 ft 6 ins in diameter, 1,020 ft in depth and was the second means of escape in an emergency. The Old Mills shaft retained the William Evans steam winding engine until closure in 1966. The William Evans steam winding engine at Springfield Colliery was removed and replaced by an electric winder which came from South Wales.

Three seams were worked at the two pits, all in the Farrington Series, The Middle, Bottom and Bright seams. The Middle Vein was 20 to 22 ins. in section. The Bottom Vein had coal 33 ins in section with a 2 in. dirt parting. The final and lowest seam was the Bright Vein 20 to 24 ins thick. All three seams had a Clift Roof and a Pan Floor (see glossary). At Nationalisation the underground conditions at Old Mills Colliery were similar to most of the pits in the coalfield — the coal was hand got, and hand loaded. There was shot firing on a limited scale.

The Middle Vein coal was worked on a longwall face. The workings section was an average of one foot nine inches of clean coal with a good roof and floor, but wet. The face normally had a gradient of 1 in 4 worked with bottom belt conveyor. Wooden supports were used but no packing or caving of the roof (to reduce the area of workings and increase the effectiveness of the ventilation) was practised. A row of cogs (a wall of wooden blocks) was erected at four yard intervals behind the conveyor, and was moved forward. The gate road was timbered with double track, and an escape road was driven 20 yards from the top end of the face.

In 1953 the details for the face in the Middle Vein were:

Length of face	*165 ft.*
Average rate of advance	*2.2 feet per day.*
Average daily output	*30 tons saleable.*
Face O.M. S. (ouput per man shift)	*26 cwts saleable.*
District O.M. S. to pit bottom	*15.8 cwts saleable.*

In 1953 the Coal Board brought in a number of engineers from South Wales who visited Old Mills Colliery and other collieries, to make recommendations for future improvements. One engineer when visiting Old Mills Colliery commented: "There was no recognisable second way out from this district. The return is very restricted and is poor condition. After travelling 200 yards of the main return, which at the best can be described as a "rat hole" and which took 40 minutes to accomplish, we decided that it not prudent to not continue further and returned to the intake via a cross cut."

At this period the ventilation in the district was said to be extremely poor, and that the air in the return was almost saturated, so the engineer felt that the district should be abandoned immediately.

In the Bottom Vein one double unit longwall face was operated with a working section of 3 ft with a dirt band in the middle 4 to 6 ins thick. This face was 270 ft long, with an average daily output of 105 saleable tons.

The coal was undercut, by two coaling shifts — days and afternoons, but the output was small due to the limitations of the haulage system. An inspector reported that "roof control was non-existent. All face supports were wooden props and lids. No supports were withdrawn, and there was no packing, except on the roads which were of poor quality."

The layout at Old Mills Colliery in the Bottom Vein district was poor, and coal was moved on a top loading conveyor, to the trunk gate where two top loading conveyors 600 and 360 ft long worked in series, since difficulties made it impossible to work a single conveyor.

From the loading station an endless haulage rope worked along the level of the main dip which was only in fair condition. At this time (1953) a development was being driven through a downthrow fault and it was recorded that the driveage had advanced only 60ft in the last three months. In the Bright Seam two districts were worked but only 34 saleable tons were obtained from the Springfield Brights face. Lack of investments clearly showed, as the right hand side of the face could only work over 90 ft since the face belt drive motor was only 5 h.p. and could not work a longer length.

These faces used an undercutter and the coal was thrown by hand on the belt. All support was of timber. Six haulage engines were needed to move coal, and the haulage system was extremely poor and expensive. The main haulage at the pit bottom had to serve both the Springfield Brights district and the Bottom Vein district. On the gate conveyor, two men worked hard shovelling an average of 35 tons per day to the discharge chute. Three faces were at work in the Brights seam; the total number of faces were five and their small daily outputs were certainly not economic. The face was eventually stopped by a fault and closed in 1953.

The colliery closed on 1 April 1966 with some of the men being transferred to Kilmersdon and Writhlington Collieries. Output figures for the colliery only survive for the years 1947 to 1950. It is noticeable that the saleable output increased under the National Coal Board from 65,341 tons in 1947 to 83,820 tons in 1950.

The abandonment plans of Old Mills Colliery also show that the colliery reserves were almost exhausted and that panels of coal were worked in the No.5 or Middle Vein and the No.7 or Bottom Vein north of the Winterfield fault around one mile north of the Springfield shaft. Workings in the No.10 or Brights seam never extended north more than 3,000 ft north of the coaling shaft and were abandoned by 1949 and never reached as far as the Paulton Hospital. A pillar of coal was left around the Paulton Printing works, and the workings never came closer than 500 ft to the south east of the works.

On the surface Old Mills and Springfield Pits had been little altered apart from the addition of the screens and washery at Springfield. The Old Mills site was particularly attractive, standing in the rolling Somerset countryside. Old Mills Colliery was never connected to the North Somerset Railway and was only linked on the surface to Springfield by a tramway which crossed the road just east of Springfield Pit.

The buildings of both pits were constructed from the stone from local lias quarries, the structures had tiled roofs with brick built chimneys. The Old Mills pithead and engine house was enclosed in a long low structure with round headed windows, as was Springfield Pit. The whole of the Old Mills Pit remained as built in 1860-61 with very little alteration, apart from the later brick and steel structure under the headframe, when the shaft was converted into an upcast shaft.

The cantilevered wooden headframes were original and, with the exception of a Yorkshire pit, were the last working wooden headframes in the country. The winding engine, built by William Evans of

Paulton Foundry in 1861, was almost unaltered, and may have been the oldest steam winding engine in use when it was taken out of use in 1966. The engine is now in store in the Bristol Industrial Museum.

The engine man drove the engine from a platform situated over and between the two cylinders; this enabled him to see the pit top and banksman. The indicator gear, was made by Llewellins & James, the brass founders of Bristol. Steam was provided by two Lancashire boilers with a third boiler as spare. The last engine man was the late Dennis Sperry of Buckland Dinham.

Today the Tesco Supermarket stands on the site of Springfield Colliery and the only feature left is the conical tip of Old Mills Colliery and the smaller tip of Springfield Pit behind the supermarket.

Old Mills and Springfield Collieries. General view of Old Mills Colliery, looking across the engine house and pithead with the training centre in background, 1965.

Pithead and engine house of Old Mills Colliery with cantilevered wooden headframe 1965.

The pithead of Springfield Pit in 1965. Although the chimney still stands the steam winding engine had been replaced with an electric winder. This pit had sidings and rail connection to the North Somerset line. This headframe was also of wooden cantilevered construction.

Left: The interior of the Springfield pithead, 1965.

Below: The demolition of the headframe of the Springfield Colliery in 1966.

Right: The markers name cast into the bed of the Old Mills winding engine. 1965.

Below: The late Dennis Sperry of Buckland Dinham at the controls of the Old Mills steam winding engine. On this engine the controls were mounted on a platform 10 feet above the engine, so that the engine man could see the pit top and banksman.

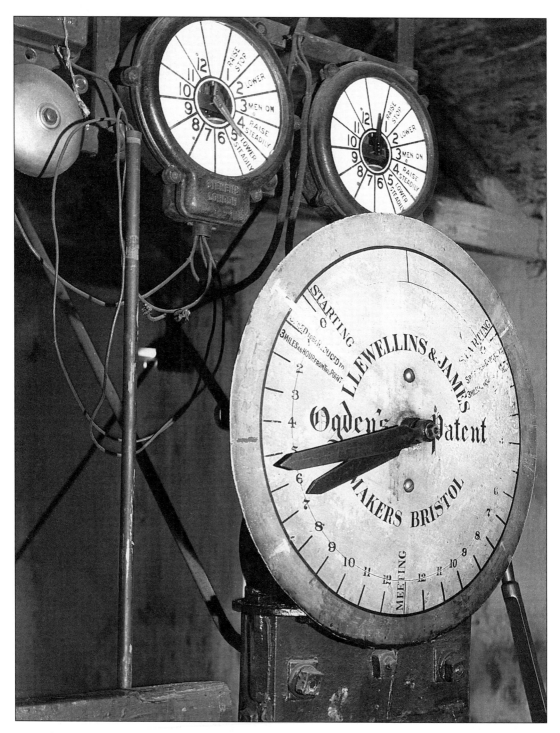

The indicator gear of the Old Mills engine which was made in
Bristol by Llewellins & James around 1860-1.

Looking along the Old Mills engine at the crank and right hand cylinder with the slide valve mounted over the cylinder. Dennis Sperry is at the controls.

Drum of the Old Mills Steam Winding Engine, note the lattice or open work eccentric rods

Two shafts were sunk in 1910 by the Pensford & Bromley Collieries Ltd, but due to excessive water the northern shaft only wound coal from an inset 750 ft from the surface. The southern shaft was also sunk to a depth of 750 ft and was used as an upcast and a second means of escape in an emergency.

The reserves in the Bromley Nos. 4 & 5 seams were large. But even before Nationalisation, it became apparent that as the seams dipped steeply away from the haulage system only a limited part of the reserves could be worked without deepening the Bromley shaft, or driving an expensive drift. It was known that water-bearing strata existed between the Pensford No. 2 and the Bromley Series and this barrier could only be passed by the costly cementation process. So it was planned some years before Nationalisation to drive an extension of the Coronation incline, and exploit the unworkable reserves. This expensive and complex project was completed and was ready to be worked just as the industry was nationalised, and certainly prolonged the life of Pensford Colliery by many years.

In the cementation process, cement is injected into the strata through bore-holes to seal the water-bearing fissures and openings, to allow driving in more or less dry ground. See page 107.

In 1953 coal was only wound on the day shift, the Pensford No.2 and the Bromley 4 and 5 seams were worked, from three main working districts, two in the Pensford No.2 seam and one in the Bromley 4 and 5 seams.

The Bromley district was reached by two cross-measure drifts which were driven west at a gradient of 1 in 3 against the dip. Where the drift reached the 4 and 5 seams, the coal was worked from Bromley Colliery. Because of a low breaking strain of the draw gear on the 11 cwt coal tubs, the safe working load was only 8 tubs of 11 cwts per journey, which meant that only 180 tons of coal could be wound up the drift in a shift.

The Jubilee District worked one face which produced approximately only 60 tons of saleable coal in a day. The North Coronation District had a cross-measure drift 1,800 ft long and dip of 1 in 3, this drift was said to be an excellent piece of driving, and kept in excellent condition, and the 110 h.p. electric endless haulage gear was capable of dealing with a very large output. The No. 1 District which was partly worked with stalls and one conveyor face 195 ft long, had a daily output of 100 tons, but the output was limited by the poor haulage.

Reports of the time speak of good roof control at Pensford, but the underground haulage system had 25 separate engines in use. The colliery was remote from others and most of the workforce had to travel by bus; a high percentage of the workforce was foreign, so even in the 1950s future recruitment looked difficult.

The future of Pensford was not good, since the only district which had a high output was the Jubilee district, which had a limited life. The replacements for the Jubilee District would be in the Bromley 4 & 5 seams or Pensford No.2 seam in the Coronation District, which would be down dip and here haulage cost were already excessively high. The Coronation District was also very disturbed geologically, the area was said to have limited life of only 5 or 6 years in 1953.

The North Coronation and No.1 District were in 1953 1 mile inbye from pit bottom, the area was badly faulted, and it was said that maintenance of conveyors was difficult and in some areas impossible. A decision was made to close the pit by 1958; the geology was so poor that mechanisation was almost impossible; the seams undulated, and were badly faulted, many haulage engines were needed, all increasing the cost of working, so the pit could never be viable. The colliery closed on the 12th December 1958.

Sinking of Pensford Pit in 1910.

The demolition of the Pensford chimney in 1959.

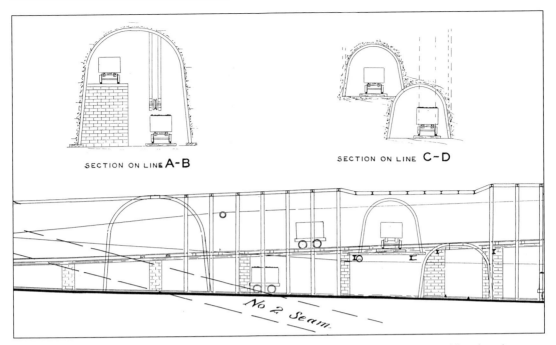

SECTION ON LINE A-B

SECTION ON LINE C-D

No 2 Seam

Above: NCB drawing of the pit bottom arrangement, showing full tubs at ground level and empties on raised tubline.

Below: Drawing of the many boreholes used in the cementation process, here the heading passed through wet broken ground, and cement was pumped under pressure into the boreholes to stabilise the poor ground. 1945 to 1946.

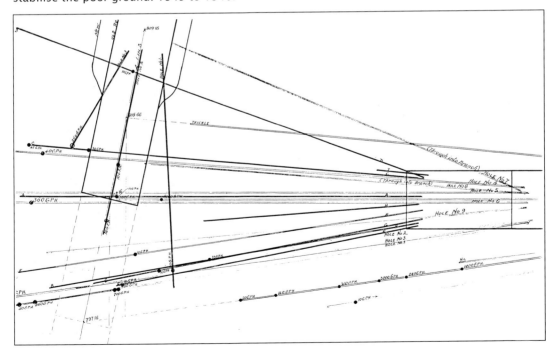

The only known photograph of a rescue in progress at the Mendip shaft sometime between 1955-62. The casualty arriving at the surface, having ascended 1,800 ft in a sinking hoppit, was attended by rescue men in breathing apparatus administering oxygen.

The casualty was Mr G. Burge, attended by W. B.Brigges, (rescue captain), Ron Flower and Bob Hudson. (Alex Hann)

Right: The rescue team in 1960 outside the Norton Hill Rescue Station. The team are wearing the Proto Oxygen type self-contained breathing apparatus. Note that every man carries a horn for signalling. The superintedent was then Alex Hann who stands in the centre. From left to right are E. S. Hedges, Dave Chedgy, Brian Cooper, Ales Hann with Terry Brown and John Kingman in the front row.

Below: The mine rescue team at the Central Rescue Station, located at the Old Norton Hill Colliery in the late 1950's. This team covered the Bristol and Somerset area, by then the only mine at Bristol was at Harry Stoke.

Fred House on the left in the white shirt was the superintendent; two of the team are wearing smoke helmets. The unknown man on the right and John Kingman at the bottom right are holding the horn used for signalling underground in poor visibility.

The headframe of the old Norton Hill Pit can be seen in the background.

A.B Machine. A Longwall under cutting machine made by Anderson Boyes, which undercuts the coal seam.

Air-Course. An underground roadway kept open for the purpose of conducting fresh air into various parts of the mine.

Banksman. A workman at the top of the pit removes the full tubs from the cage and puts empty tubs into the cage.

Bell-Mould. A stone which is the stem of the plant Sigillaria, which has a larger diameter downwards. They have very smooth surface and they are apt to drop out suddenly.

Boards. A certain type of stone which lies above the coal seam.

Branch. A stone-drift tunnel made in solid rock.

Broken. The part of the mine were the coal is worked away, also known as the gob.

Cementation. A system of drilling bore holes in to poor ground, and injecting cement into the boreholes.

Clift Roof. An Argillaceous shale.

Clod. A Somerset term for a softish stone, which lies over the seam, and invariably falls after the coal is taken.

Cogs. A timber structure normally used to support the roof.

Colliery take. The area which had been or was intended to be worked from a particular colliery.

Dipple. A heading driven towards the dip or deep.

Down dip. The area where the seams dips down away from the surface.

Drift. A sloping tunnel driven into the coal seams. Used where a shaft is not needed.

Engine Pit. A shaft on which the pumping engine is placed.

Pan Floor. The fire clay lying under the coal seams worked at Radstock and the neighbourhood.

Pillar of coal. Unworked area of coal normally left under a church or large house.

Slant. Dipping tunnel driven into the coal measures, to work and remove output of mine.

Stall. Part of the Pillar and stall system where one workman and assistant would cut out a workings place at right angles to the heading.

Stone Drift. See branch.

Trunk road or Gate Road. Main underground roadway often used as air intake and carried conveyors or underground tram way.

Undercutting machine. A machine which cuts a slot in the lower section of the coal seam, allowing the collier to bring down the mass of coal.

Panels. An area of worked coal usually rectangular served by roads on either side of the panel known as gate roads.

Plough. A post war device for winning the coal, which was dragged along the coal face shearing off the coal.

Putt. A shallow wooden box used for hauling the coal from the face. Held from 3 to 6 cwt of coal, when empty it weighs 60 pounds.

Trepanner. A later form of coal cutting machine not used in Somerset.

OMS. Output per manshift.

Loads creeper to screens tippler. No 2 Winding Engine House in the background, Kilmersdon Colliery

INDEX